THE SEVEN LAST WORDS FROM

HEINRICH SCHÜTZ

NOTES FOR PERFORMANCE

The Part of Jesus. This was originally to be accompanied by two viols and continuo. In this edition the original two-viol accompaniment is identical with the top stave of the organ part A (three staves).

If strings are present (the viol parts may be played by two violins or violin and viola), this top stave must be omitted from the organ, with the result that the organ part may then be played on a single-manual instrument, with or without pedals.

If strings are not present, organ part A must be played on two manuals with pedals, the second manual part being set out so as to be easily playable by the left hand. The alternative small notes, which avoid inartistic doublings, are to be played only if there are no strings; that is to say, when the organ is responsible for both viols (R.H.) and continuo (L.H. and pedal).

There is also an alternative organ part B on two staves for a single-manual instrument with or without pedals. This part must not be used if strings are present.

The string parts are on hire.

Accompaniment. Organ chords may often be played shorter than notated, according to the discretion of the player. This principle applies also to any string continuo instrument, although not to such a great extent.

Ornamentation. The solo vocal parts may be ornamented, providing this is done with restraint and in accordance with the style of the period. Only the mildest decoration has been indicated in the organ accompaniment, and more may be used if desired, particularly when strings are used for the part of Jesus, and the organ is playing the harmonies only (second manual and pedals of organ part A). It is, however, recommended that extra decoration be used very sparingly, and that great care be taken never to draw attention to the continuo away from the solos and obbligato parts, but only to illustrate or underline what is going on in these parts. A perfectly satisfactory performance may be obtained by playing and singing the parts exactly as written.

Symphonia. The symphonia following the first chorus and preceding the last was originally scored for instruments (five parts). Schütz did not specify the particular instruments to be used, and it is here printed for organ solo (part A with pedals, part B for manuals only). Scores and parts of the symphonia for two violins (and/or two oboes), viola I, viola II (or cello), cello and bass, together with an organ continuo part, are on hire. Optional parts for two tenor trombones and bassoon (or bass trombone) are also on hire. It is urged that any brass instruments should avoid the use of vibrato.

Continuo. An optional cello or viola da gamba continuo part, which may be used throughout the work, is on hire. Alternatively it is possible to play from the vocal score by following the bass line of the accompaniment throughout (of organ part A for the part of Jesus).

Vocal Parts. The central narrative consists of twenty-five short solos and quartets. The part of the Evangelist is sung variously by alto, tenor I, and soprano, and a group of mixed voices. The voices change to mark the break between each of the seven sayings of Jesus. No breaks should be made within the sections.

The whole of this central narrative should be sung in fairly strict time, as it is not true recitative.

The second tenor part in the Introduction and Conclusion may be sung by baritones, as the highest note is E.

EDITORIAL NOTES

It has been considered vitally important to preserve Schütz's note values wherever possible, especially because there is so much monody over a static bass in this type of work. For this reason, although every effort has been made to keep to well-known biblical texts, some passages have had to be adapted. For example, the most commonly known biblical text corresponding to the German 'Es ist vollbracht' is 'It is finished', but the editors found it necessary to change this to 'It is fulfilled' in order to preserve Schütz's stress. In the few places where it was found necessary to change the note values small notes show the original, fitting the German text.

Schütz's figuring is obviously incomplete, and those figures in brackets indicate either Schütz's own implied harmonies, or the editor's suggestions.

Duration 22 minutes

THE SEVEN LAST WORDS FROM THE CROSS

INTROITUS
(Chorus)

HEINRICH SCHÜTZ
(1585-1672)

The Seven Last Words From The Cross

The Seven Last Words From The Cross

4

The Seven Last Words From The Cross

The Seven Last Words From The Cross

SYMPHONIA

★(Organ part **A**)

★ See page 7 for organ part **B** of Symphonia (manuals only)

The Seven Last Words From The Cross

SYMPHONIA

(Organ part **B**, for manuals only)

EVANGELIST (ALTO)

And it was at about the third hour that they cru - ci - fied Je - sus, and He thus spake:
Und es war um die drit - te Stun-de, da sie Je - sum kreu - zig - ten, er a - ber sprach:

The Seven Last Words From The Cross

8

The Seven Last Words From The Cross

9

The Seven Last Words From The Cross

10

The Seven Last Words From The Cross

12

16

And thou, and thou, dost ___ thou, dost thou not fear God, as thou
Und du, und du fürch - test dich auch nicht für Gott, der du

art in the same con-dem-na - tion? For we, we are just-ly con-
doch in glei - cher Ver-dam - niss bist, und zwar wir sind bil - lig dar-

-demn'd and are re-ceiv - ing ___ the due re - ward of our ___ deeds:
- in - nen, denn wir emp-fan - gen ___ was uns-re Ta - ten wert ___ sind,

17

but ___ this man, but ___ this man ___ hath done no - thing, done no-thing a - miss.
die - ser a - ber, die - ser a - ber ___ hat nichts un - ge-schick-tes ge-han - delt.

The Seven Last Words From The Cross

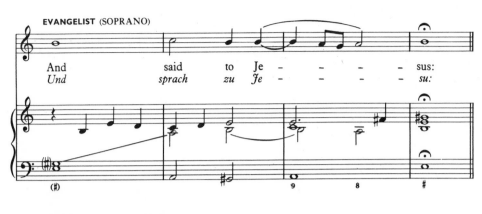

EVANGELIST (SOPRANO)

And said to Je - - - - - sus:
Und sprach zu Je - - - - - su:

MALEFACTOR ON THE RIGHT (BASS)

Lord, re-mem-ber me, Lord, Lord, re-mem-ber me, Lord, re-mem-ber
Herr ge-den-ke an mich, Herr, Herr ge-den-ke an mich, Herr ge-den-ke an

me when thou gain-est thy king - dom.
mich, wenn du in dein Reich kommst.

EVANGELIST (SOPRANO)

And Je - sus said:
Und Je - sus sprach:

The Seven Last Words From The Cross

14

JESUS (TENOR II)
20

Tru - ly I say to thee, this day shalt thou be with
Wahr - lich, ich sa - ge dir, heu - te wirst du mit

me in Pa - - ra - dise, in Pa - - ra - dise.
mir im Pa - ra - dies___ sein, im Pa - ra - dies___ sein.

The Seven Last Words From The Cross

JESUS (TENOR II)

E - li, E - li, E - - - - li, la - ma
E - li, E - li, E - - - - li, la - ma

sa - bach - tha - ni, E - - - - li, la - ma
a - sab - tha - ni, E - - - - li, la - ma

sa-bach-tha - ni, la-ma sa-bach-tha - - - - ni?
a - sab-tha - ni, la-ma a - sab-tha - - - - ni?

EVANGELIST (S.A.T.B.)

Which is in - ter - pre - ted:
Das ist ver - dol - met - schet:

The Seven Last Words From The Cross

JESUS (TENOR II)

My___ God, my___ God, my___ God, my God, wherefore,
Mein___ Gott, mein___ Gott, mein___ Gott, mein Gott, wa-rum,

wherefore hast thou me for-sa-ken, my___ God, my God, where-fore
wa-rum hast du mich ver-las-sen, mein___ Gott, mein Gott, wa-rum

hast thou me for - sa - ken, wherefore hast thou me for-sa - - - - ken?
hast du mich ver - las-sen, wa-rum hast du mich ver-las - - - - sen?

A

B

EVANGELIST (ALTO)

24

And straight - way Je - sus, knowing that now all was ac-com-plish'd, all was ac-com-
Dar - nach___ als Je - sus wuss-te, dass schon al - les voll-bracht, al - les voll-bracht

- plish'd, that the scrip - ture might be ful - fill'd, He___ saith:
war, dass die Schrift er - fül - let wür - de, sprach___ er:

20

The Seven Last Words From The Cross

The Seven Last Words From The Cross

The Seven Last Words From The Cross

EVANGELIST (S.A.T.B.)

24

SYMPHONIA
as before (page 6)

The Seven Last Words From The Cross

CONCLUSIO

(Chorus)

26

The Seven Last Words From The Cross

The Seven Last Words From The Cross

The Seven Last Words From The Cross

The Seven Last Words From The Cross

Printed in England by
Caligraving Limited Thetford Norfolk

OXFORD UNIVERSITY PRESS